# The Tale of Joseph and his Brothers

# Other brilliant stories to collect:

# The Tale of Joseph and his Brothers

*Retold by*
Tony Bradman

*Illustrated by*
Michael Terry

**■ SCHOLASTIC**
Home of the Story

Scholastic Children's Books,
Commonwealth House, 1–19 New Oxford Street,
London WC1A 1NU, UK
a division of Scholastic Ltd
London ~ New York ~ Toronto ~ Sydney ~ Auckland
Mexico City ~ New Delhi ~ Hong Kong

First published by Scholastic Ltd, 2000

Text copyright © Tony Bradman, 2000
Illustrations copyright © Michael Terry, 2000

ISBN 0 439 01484 0

Printed by Cox and Wyman Ltd, Reading, Berks.

2 4 6 8 10 9 7 5 3 1

The right of Tony Bradman and Michael Terry to be identified as the
author and illustrator respectively of this work has been asserted by
them in accordance with the Copyright, Designs and Patents Act, 1988.

Once, a long, long time ago, in the land of Canaan, a man called Jacob had twelve sons. That's right, twelve — and it wasn't exactly a case of the more the merrier. In fact, there was plenty of jealousy among them, so you won't be surprised to hear this

story is about trouble in the family. Big trouble.

It all started because Jacob made the kind of mistake fathers shouldn't. He had a favourite son, which was bad enough. But he let the others know who it was, and as you can imagine, that stirred up lots of ill feeling in them.

They were called Reuben, Simeon, Levi, Judah, Issachar, Zebulun, Dan, Naphtali, Gad, Asher, and lastly Joseph and Benjamin, these two being the youngest. Between them, the twelve had four different mothers, Joseph and Benjamin's being Rachel, who had died. And Joseph was Jacob's favourite.

Now it has to be said Joseph was a bright lad. He was full of clever ideas for running the family business better – they were shepherds, kept goats as well, grew a few crops on the side – and Jacob always listened to him.

"That boy will go far," Jacob was often heard to say, a smile on his face.

"As far away as possible, we hope," the others would mutter darkly.

But Jacob didn't hear, and Joseph was too busy trying to impress his father to worry about his brothers. In any case, he thought they were pretty useless, and tittle-tattled to Jacob whenever they lost a sheep, or a goat died.

None of which made Joseph very popular. In fact, his brothers hated him, and they grew to loathe him even more when Jacob gave him a special

present, a flashy coat of many colours. Then there were the dreams...

Joseph had dreams like nobody else ever had done, or ever would.

"Hey, listen to this, you lot," Joseph said cockily to his brothers one day. "I had an amazing dream last night. We were binding sheaves in the fields, and your eleven bowed down to my one. What do you make of that?"

"Oh, so you think you're going to rule over us?" said his brothers angrily.

Joseph took no notice, and the next day, he told them another dream.

"It was incredible," he said to his brothers more cockily than before. "This time the sun, and the moon, and eleven stars bowed down to me..."

Joseph's brothers were speechless, and even Jacob thought he'd gone a

little too far. But Jacob didn't realize how bad things really were in the family. Otherwise he wouldn't have sent Joseph to check on his brothers again a few days later, when they were out together, feeding the flocks.

Joseph's brothers had been discussing him. They'd all had enough of his arrogance, and wanted to be rid of him somehow. Suddenly they saw

him approaching in the distance —
and somebody suggested they should
kill him.

"We could say he was eaten by a
wild animal," another one said, and
there was a murmur of agreement.
"Then we'll see how his big dreams
turn out!"

But Reuben said it would be wrong,
and he was the oldest. So when Joseph
arrived, his brothers only grabbed him,
and stripped him of his fancy coat, and
threw him into a well. Reuben went off
to check on the flocks, and the rest ate
their lunch. They argued for ages

about what to do with Joseph.

Then a caravan of traders on camels passed by, and Judah had an idea.

"Why don't we sell him to them as a slave?" he said. "At least that way we'd be rid of him without having a brother's blood on our hands."

And that's what they did. They dragged Joseph out of the well, and didn't listen to his pleas as they sold

him to the traders. When Reuben returned, he was horrified to discover what they'd done ... but the caravan was long gone.

So the brothers killed a young goat, dipped Joseph's coat of many colours in the blood, and took it home with them to their father. Then they told him that Joseph had gone missing, and that they couldn't find him anywhere.

"We did find this, though, Father," they said, and showed Jacob the coat. "We're not sure, but we think this might be the coat you gave Joseph..."

"It is, it is!" wailed Jacob. "Some wild beast must have devoured him!"

Jacob plunged into the deepest mourning. He tore his clothes and wept for days. And no matter what his sons said or did, Jacob would not be consoled.

Joseph, of course, knew nothing of this. His troubles were just beginning. The traders who had bought him

were travelling to Egypt, and there they sold him to the captain of Pharaoh's guard, a powerful man called Potiphar.

Joseph was pretty shocked by what had happened. It seemed that one minute he'd been a favourite, lording it over his brothers, and the next he was the lowliest slave in a strange land. But he was still the same Joseph.

Soon he was full of ideas for running Potiphar's household better — which slave should do what, how to keep rats out of the grain store — and Potiphar listened. In fact, Potiphar thought he was wonderful, and put him in charge.

The problem was ... Potiphar's wife thought Joseph was wonderful too.

"Joseph," she said one day, catching him by his sleeve. Potiphar was not at home, and there was nobody else in the house. "I want you to kiss me."

"But you are my master's wife," said Joseph angrily, "and he has been good to me. So how can I do such a

wicked thing? It would be a sin."

And with that, Joseph pulled away from her, leaving most of his sleeve behind. She was angry too, and worried in case Joseph should tell Potiphar what she had done. So she told Potiphar Joseph had tried to kiss her, showed him the sleeve ... and Potiphar had Joseph thrown into Pharaoh's prison.

"Let that be a lesson to you!" said Potiphar as the jailer locked Joseph in.

Joseph sat alone in his cell, and brooded. Here he was, in desperate straits once again. He must be doing something very wrong, he thought. Perhaps he ought to change ... but for the time being, he was still the same Joseph.

So soon he was full of ideas for running the prison better – which guard should do what job, how to keep the prisoners busy – and the jailer listened. In fact, the jailer thought Joseph was wonderful, and made him chief trusty.

Now not long after that, two new

prisoners were brought in. The first was Pharaoh's butler, and the second was his baker, and they had both upset their master for some reason or another. Joseph was put in charge of them.

One morning, Joseph took in their breakfasts, and the pair looked even gloomier than usual. Joseph asked why. It appeared they had each dreamed a strange dream, and nobody could tell them what their dreams might mean.

"I'm good with dreams," said Joseph, feeling strange himself. "I'll try..."

"Well," said the butler uncertainly, "I dreamed of a vine which had three branches. The vine budded and blossomed and produced grapes, and then I took the grapes and I pressed them into Pharaoh's cup and gave it to him."

To his surprise, Joseph saw straight away what the dream meant.

"The three branches stand for three days," he said with a smile, "and that's

how much longer you'll be in this prison. Then Pharaoh will forgive you and take you back, and you'll give him his cup again, just as you did before."

As you can imagine, the butler thought this was terrific news, and thanked Joseph for his interpretation. Joseph simply asked the butler to put in a good word for him with Pharaoh once he got out, and the butler said he would.

Now the baker was looking forward to hearing his dream explained.

"Right, here goes," he said cheerfully. "In my dream, I had three baskets stacked up on my head, and in the topmost one there were cakes and bread for Pharaoh. Then a flock of birds came down and ate everything."

To his dismay, Joseph saw straight away what this dream meant too.

"The three baskets stand for three days," he said sadly. "And that's how much longer you'll be in this prison. But Pharaoh won't forgive you and take you back. You'll be

hanged instead ... and birds will eat your flesh."

The baker's smile turned stiff — and three days later, so did the rest of him. For Joseph had been right about both dreams. Pharaoh forgave the butler and restored him to his place, but he hanged the baker ... and Joseph saw it all.

The butler forgot about him, and the prison days dragged slowly by.

Two years later, somebody else dreamed some strange dreams. It was Pharaoh, and he asked all his wise men to tell him what the dreams meant. But they didn't have a clue, and Pharaoh definitely wasn't very happy.

Then the butler remembered Joseph — and Joseph was quickly sent for.

Now Joseph was a bright lad, and he saw that this might be his chance to save himself. So he put on clean clothes, and was taken to Pharaoh's great chamber. Joseph bowed down before the mighty ruler and his court.

"I hear you're good with dreams,"

said Pharaoh. "Well, I've had two dreams stranger than any I've ever had before. Can you explain them?"

"I'll ... I'll do my best, your m-m-majesty," said Joseph nervously.

"In the first dream," said Pharaoh, "I was standing on the bank of the Nile, and seven fat cows came up out of the river. Then seven thin cows followed them, and the thin cows ate up the fat ones, but they stayed just as thin."

"I see," said Joseph. "And what happened in the second dream?"

"That was even stranger," said Pharaoh. "I saw seven full ears of

wheat grow on a single stalk, followed by seven thin ears. They looked as if they'd been blasted empty by the east wind. Then the thin ears ate the full ears..."

To his relief, Joseph saw straight away what the dreams meant.

"The dreams are the same," he said confidently. "God's shown you what he'll do. The seven fat cows and

full ears are seven years of plenty,
to be followed by seven years of
thin cows and thin ears ... a famine in
the land."

There were sharp intakes of breath all
round at Joseph's words, and lots of
muttering as he told Pharaoh the full
horror of what he foresaw. The seven
years of plenty would be forgotten in
seven years of terrible hunger.

"Such a change!" murmured Pharaoh

at last. "It can't happen, can it?"

"Believe me," said Joseph, who of course knew how dramatically things could change in life, "it can, and it will. But you could still do something about it. God's given you a warning ... and I have a plan that might help."

Joseph's plan was simple. He said they should save some food during the

coming years of plenty, so they would have it in the years of famine. And he thought it might be a good idea if somebody oversaw the operation...

"I think I know just the man for the job," said Pharaoh, who was very impressed with this Hebrew slave. In fact, he thought Joseph was wonderful, so he put him in charge of running his household ... and the whole country.

Joseph was pretty amazed by what had happened. It seemed that one minute he'd been a slave, and the next he was lording it over those who had been his masters. And he wasn't quite the same Joseph any more.

He got married, for a start, to a girl called Asenath, and they had two sons, Manasseh and Ephraim, so he had to learn how to be a father himself. And as he travelled the land, making sure enough food was stored for the future, Joseph learned more about taking care of business, and he did very well.

He almost forgot the past, and the years of plenty flew swiftly by.

Then the years of famine began, as Joseph had said, and people went hungry in every country except Egypt. Joseph opened all the storehouses, and people journeyed from far and wide to buy the food he'd saved.

They even came from distant Canaan, where the famine was very

hard. Jacob was still living there with eleven of his sons, and he sent ten to Egypt to buy corn. He insisted that Benjamin, his youngest, should stay behind.

"Just in case something ... bad might happen to him," said Jacob darkly.

So the other brothers went with their asses to Egypt, and asked to see the man in charge. They bowed down

before him in Pharaoh's palace, and
didn't recognize this powerful
Egyptian, for that's what Joseph had
become.

But Joseph recognized them instant-
ly, and remembered the nights when
he'd dreamed of them, and the wrong
they'd done to him. He realized they
didn't know who he was, and spoke
roughly to them through an interpreter.

"You didn't come here to buy
food," he said. "You're ... spies!"

"But ... but we aren't, my Lord!"
said Reuben. They were all terrified
now. "We're simple shepherds, ten of

twelve brothers from the land of Canaan. The youngest is at home with our father, and the second youngest is dead..."

"I don't want to hear any more," snapped Joseph suddenly. He had them kept under guard for three days. Then he came to speak to them again.

"Very well, prove to me that what you say is true," he said. "You can have the corn, but one of you has to stay here, and to get the hostage released, the rest have to come back with this ... youngest brother. Do we have a deal?"

The interpreter translated, and the brothers muttered to each other in their own language. They didn't know, of course, that Joseph could understand.

"We've brought this on ourselves!" somebody hissed. "We didn't listen when Joseph begged us not to sell him, did we? Now we're being punished!"

At that moment, Joseph nearly

gave himself away. He had to turn so they couldn't see the tears in his eyes ... but he managed to pull himself together.

Eventually the brothers agreed to Joseph's terms. So he took Simeon as hostage, and ordered the sacks they'd brought on their asses to be filled with corn. But Joseph secretly ordered the money they'd paid to be put back in the sacks. And when they discovered it on the way home, they were afraid.

As you can imagine, Jacob definitely wasn't very happy, either.

The nine sons who returned told their father what had happened, and how the powerful man they'd met had taken Simeon hostage, and wouldn't release him unless they returned with Benjamin, to prove he existed.

"Over my dead body," said Jacob flatly. "What is it with you boys? Every time you go out to do something you come back with one less brother. First Joseph, now Simeon...

I'm blowed if I'll lose another son the same way."

But the famine went on and on, and they soon got through all the corn the brothers had brought from Egypt. Eventually, Jacob said they would have to go and buy more – and the brothers said they wouldn't go without Benjamin.

"There's no point otherwise," said

Judah. "That man told us we wouldn't be allowed to see him if we didn't take our youngest brother. But I promise I'll look after him, Father. You can blame me if I don't bring him back..."

Jacob realized he had no choice ... and gave in. He did insist on sending presents for this powerful Egyptian, though, as well as the original payment, in case there'd been some kind of a mistake, plus enough for more corn.

And he still had a heavy heart as he watched his sons ride away.

They didn't feel too cheerful themselves when they stood once more before Joseph in his great chamber. Joseph ordered that they be taken to his house, where he would eat with them at noon — and they started to panic.

"He must know about the money," somebody muttered guiltily as they were being led away by Joseph's steward.

"I'll bet he's just waiting for a chance to seize all our stuff, and make us his slaves," said somebody else.

At Joseph's house, they simply couldn't contain themselves. They told the steward about the money, and how they'd brought it back. But he told them to relax — he said he remembered collecting the money for the corn himself, so what they'd found in their sacks must have been a gift from God.

There was no time for more questions, or talk. The steward handed

Simeon over to his brothers, and then Joseph arrived. The brothers gave him the presents they'd brought with them, and bowed down to him again.

Joseph played it cool ... very cool indeed.

"I trust you're well," he said. The interpreter translated, and the brothers nodded, terrified, and said they were. "And didn't you say something about an elderly father?" Joseph continued. "Is the old man still going strong?"

"Oh yes, your honour," murmured

the brothers. "He's in good health."

"And I suppose this is the youngest brother you mentioned," said Joseph.

He glanced at Benjamin, and suddenly his brother's face reminded him of his mother and father, and his home, and at that moment Joseph almost gave himself away again. But he made some excuse, and went to another room and wept alone for a while. Then he

returned, in control once more.

Joseph had food and drink brought, and made sure that Benjamin got the most. The brothers all ate and drank, and were amazed to find themselves laughing and joking with this man who had them in his power. Joseph left them after a while ... but spoke secretly to his steward on his way out.

"Have each man's sack filled with

as much food as he can carry," said Joseph quietly. "Put their money in each sack too. And while you're at it, put my special silver cup in the sack that belongs to the youngest."

The steward did as Joseph ordered, and in the morning, the brothers set off on the return journey to Canaan. Then before they'd ridden far, Joseph told his steward to take some

men and go after them, and ask why they'd stolen his cup. The brothers were totally confused, and denied everything.

"You've got the wrong men," somebody said. "We brought that money back, didn't we? So why would we steal from your master, in God's name?"

"Search us," said somebody else, "and if you find it in one of our sacks, you can kill the brother it belongs to, and make the rest of us your slaves."

"Very well," replied the steward. "As you wish..."

So his men speedily took the sacks from each ass and searched them, starting with Reuben's. And of course, they found the cup in Benjamin's.

As you can imagine, the brothers were definitely not very happy. In fact, they were more terrified than ever when they were brought before Joseph. Judah was the only one of the eleven who could find the courage to speak.

"What can I say, your honour?" he murmured. "We're at your mercy."

"Forget it," said Joseph. "I'll keep the one who stole my cup to be my slave, but as for the rest — you can return in peace to your father."

"Please, my lord," begged Judah. "We only brought our youngest brother because you told us to. Our father didn't want him to come. He's never got over losing our other brother, and if we go back without Benjamin, it's bound to kill him. I couldn't bear that. Keep me as your slave instead."

Judah's words were too much for Joseph. Suddenly, he called out to his servants to leave the chamber, and he finally stood alone before his brothers. Then he wept loud enough for everyone in Pharaoh's palace to hear him.

"Don't you recognize me?" he said at last. "I'm Joseph, your brother. Is our father really still alive?" Joseph's brothers looked fearfully at each

other, and said nothing. "It's true," said Joseph. "I am the brother you sold into slavery, but don't worry. I'm sure it was all part of God's plan..."

Joseph had done a lot of thinking, and now he believed God had planned to save his father and his family through him. For there had only been two years of famine so far, which meant there were five years to go. Joseph had

realized his family would never make it through the harder years to come.

Not unless they came to live in Egypt, that is – the country which had plenty of food because a certain bright lad had been sent there by God. A bright lad who had suffered and learned, and become a father, and a man who could arrange things ... and a brother who could forgive and forget.

So Joseph and his brothers finally made peace with each other.

Joseph kissed his brothers, and they kissed him, and he hugged Benjamin and cried, and Benjamin hugged him back and cried too. Then they talked.

And that's the end of the story, except to say when Jacob heard the news he was so amazed he nearly fainted, and

he was thrilled to think he'd be with Joseph again before he died. Maybe he did some thinking, too ... at any rate, his other sons were happy to take their families and flocks to Egypt.

As far as they could see, it was definitely a case of the more the merrier.

Other stories to collect:

# Aesop's Fables

## Malorie Blackman
*Illustrated by Patrice Aggs*

Once upon a time there was a man named Aesop
who told stories full of wisdom…

# Hansel and Gretel

## Henrietta Branford
*Illustrated by Lesley Harker*

Once upon a time there were a brother and sister
who were left alone in the forest…

# The Snow Queen

Berlie Doherty

*Illustrated by Siân Bailey*

Once upon a time there was a little boy whose
heart was turned to ice...

# The Twelve
# Dancing Princesses

Anne Fine

*Illustrated by Debi Gliori*

Once upon a time there were twelve princesses,
and no one knew why their shoes were full
of holes...

# Grey Wolf,
# Prince Jack
# and the Firebird

Alan Garner

*Illustrated by James Mayhew*

Once upon a time there was a prince who set out
to seek the mysterious firebird…

# Mossycoat

Philip Pullman

*Illustrated by Peter Bailey*

Once upon a time there was a beautiful girl whose
mother made her a magical, mossy coat…

# Cockadoodle-doo, Mr Sultana!

Michael Morpurgo
*Illustrated by Michael Foreman*

Once upon a time there was a rich and greedy
sultan who met a clever little cockerel...

# Rapunzel

Jacqueline Wilson
*Illustrated by Nick Sharratt*

Once upon a time there was a baby who was
stolen by a witch...

# The Six Swan Brothers

Adèle Geras

*Illustrated by Ian Beck*

Once upon a time there was a brave princess
who saw her six brothers turned into swans…

# The Three Heads
# in the Well

Susan Gates

*Illustrated by Sue Heap*

Once upon a time there were two stepsisters —
one good, one bad — who both went out to seek
their fortunes…

# Rumpelstiltskin

## Kit Wright

### *Illustrated by Ted Dewan*

Once upon a time there was a beautiful girl who
would die if she couldn't spin straw into gold...

# The Goose Girl

## Gillian Cross

### *Illustrated by Jason Cockcroft*

Once upon a time there was a princess who lost
everything she had ever owned...

# The Pied Piper

K M Peyton

*Illustrated by Victor Ambrus*

Once upon a time there was a town infested
with a plague of horrible rats…

# Puss in Boots

Diana Wynne Jones

*Illustrated by Fangorn*

Once upon a time there was a handsome miller's
son who owned a very clever cat…